JIM DAVIS 8-3
YOU'RE UGLY
© 1994 PAWS, INC./Distributed by Universal Press Syndicate
BARK BARK BARK ARK BARK B B,
AS IF IT'S MY FAULT

I SPENT THE DAY DOING GOOD DEEDS
JIM DAVIS 8-8
© 1994 PAWS, INC./Distributed by Universal Press Syndicate
WHILE **YOU** DIDN'T MOVE FROM THAT SPOT
WE BOTH MADE THE WORLD A LITTLE NICER ODAY
HEY!

YOU'RE AS LIGHT AS A FEATHER!
© 1994 PAWS, INC./Distributed by Universal Press Syndicate
A REALLY, REALLY, **REALLY** BIG FEATHER
JIM DAVIS 8-18

POOR JON...
JIM DAVIS 7-21
HE'S THE KIND OF GUY WHO'LL GIVE YOU THE SHIRT OFF HIS BACK
© 1994 PAWS, INC./Distributed by Universal Press Syndicate
AND THERE ARE NO TAKERS

Garfield's

Guide To INSULTS

JIM DAVIS

RAVETTE PUBLISHING

I LIKE TO THINK OF MYSELF AS A ROLE MODEL FOR YOU BOYS
JIM DAVIS 7-23
© 1994 PAWS, INC./Distributed by Universal Press Syndicate
URF?
YES, THAT MEANS WE GET TO BLAME EVERYTHING ON HIM

I WISH I WERE BETTER LOOKING
© 1994 United Feature Syndicate, Inc
NOW, NOW. THERE'S NO REASON FOR YOU TO DO THAT
I'M THE ONE WHO SHOULD WISH YOU WERE BETTER LOOKING
JIM DAVIS 3-8

FIRST THERE WAS THE HORRIFYING "BRAIN SUCKERS FROM MARS"
JIM DAVIS 7-5
THEN IT WAS "NIGHT OF THE LIVING TOAD SNATCHERS"
© 1993 United Feature Syndicate, Inc.
WHAT DO YOU THINK?
NOW IT'S "THE WARDROBE THAT WOULDN'T DIE"

Y'KNOW GARFIELD I'M GETTING BETTER LOOKING AS I GET OLDER!
AND FOR GOOD REASON
© 1993 United Feature Syndicate, Inc.
YOUR EYESIGHT IS GOING!
JIM DAVIS 7-9

GARFIELD, AM I A GEEK?
YES
TOO BAD CATS CAN'T TALK
YES! YES! I'M SAYING YES HERE!
JIM DAVIS 3-7
© 1994 United Feature Syndicate, Inc.

JIM DAVIS 3-5
KIDS, DON'T LET THIS HAPPEN TO YOU
© 1994 United Feature Syndicate, Inc.

I REALLY NEED TO CHANGE MY IMAGE, GARFIELD
I FULLY AGREE
CHANGE CAN BE A HEALTHY THING
YOU COULDN'T BE MORE RIGHT
© 1994 United Feature Syndicate, Inc.
WE COULD BOTH STAND TO IMPROVE OUR LOOKS A LITTLE, RIGHT?
SPEAK FOR YOURSELF, DONKEY FACE
JIM DAVIS 3-10

HEY, LOOK! A BIG, FAT, DUMB CAT!
GET OUT OF HERE, YOU STUPID, UGLY TUB OF LARD
YEAH, BEAT IT!
© 1994 United Feature Syndicate, Inc.
WHATEVER HAPPENED TO "CHIRP, CHIRP"?
JIM DAVIS 3-4

GARFIELD, I'VE BEEN LOOKING AT MYSELF IN THE MIRROR
AND, I HAVE TO ASK YOU A QUESTION
AM I MACHO?
HE APPARENTLY DOESN'T NOTICE I HAVE A MOUTHFUL OF FOOD
JIM DAVIS 3-9
© 1994 United Feature Syndicate, Inc

YOU KNOW, GARFIELD...
I WISH I HAD A SECRET IDENTITY LIKE SUPER-HEROES DO
YOUR IDENTITY **IS** A SECRET
JIM DAVIS 3-12
© 1994 United Feature Syndicate, Inc.

YOU'RE FAT
© 1994 United Feature Syndicate, Inc.
AND LAZY
SEE? I'M DOING THE WORK OF TWO CATS!
JIM DAVIS 3-15

I'M TRYING TO WRITE MY AUTOBIOGRAPHY
© 1994 United Feature Syndicate, Inc.
IT'S NOT GOING VERY WELL
SOUNDS ACCURATE
JIM DAVIS 1-27

JIM DAVIS 1-28
JON, YOU NEED TO GET OUT MORE
YOU NEED TO BE WITH YOUR OWN KIND!
© 1994 United Feature Syndicate, Inc.
PROVIDED WE CAN LOCATE A THREE-TOED SLOTH WHO COLLECTS STAMPS

NOBODY PUSHES YOU AROUND, DO THEY, GARFIELD?
NOPE
© 1994 United Feature Syndicate, Inc.
NOT WITHOUT A FORKLIFT, ANYWAY
ACK! I DIDN'T SEE THAT ONE COMING
SLAP!
JIM DAVIS 2-7

JIM DAVIS 2·21
I'VE BEEN DIETING
RIIIIIGHT
NO, REALLY. IS THIS A FACE THAT WOULD LIE?
HOW SHOULD I KNOW? I'VE NEVER SEEN IT
© 1994 United Feature Syndicate, Inc.

JIM DAVIS 4·25
NYAH! NYAH! NYAH! NYAH!
MIKEY, IT'S NOT NICE TO MAKE FUN OF PEOPLE, EVEN THOUGH THEY ARE TRAVELING IN THIRD-CLASS
NO! GARFIELD, NO!
LET ME HURT'EM JUST A LITTLE BIT!
© 1984 United Feature Syndicate, Inc.

ODIE, HOW CAN YOU BE SO STUPID?
JIM DAVIS 1-4-94
© 1993 United Feature Syndicate, Inc.
WELL, IF YOU'VE GOT A PERMIT, I GUESS IT'S OKAY

ODIE! GET AWAY FROM THAT TREE! GARFIELD! GET OUT OF THAT SAND TRAP!
JIM DAVIS 5-1
WOULD YOU MIND OBSERVING PROPER GOLF ETIQUETTE THERE, MISTER?
© 1984 United Feature Syndicate, Inc.
I'M SORRY, BUT MY PETS ARE DRIVING ME NUTS
IT'S THE OUTFIT I'M TALKING ABOUT

YAWN
GASP!
WAKING UP TO MY OWN BAD BREATH IS BAD ENOUGH, BUT SOMEONE ELSE'S IS UNBEARABLE
3-6
JIM DAVIS
© 1984 United Feature Syndicate, Inc.

HERE COMES **FATSO**!
HE'S NOT ONLY FAT, HE'S SLOW
I WAS REFERRING TO YOU!
JIM DAVIS 5-13
© 1994 United Feature Syndicate, Inc.

SAY, FRIEND, ARE YOU CONSIDERED AN IDIOT?
JIM DAVIS 11-18
THEN WE HAVE JUST THE PRODUCT FOR YOU!
© 1993 United Feature Syndicate, Inc.
I HAVE THREE OF THOSE
FIGURES

THERE ARE A THOUSAND REASONS WHY I WOULDN'T WANT TO BE A DOG
JIM DAVIS 11-26
© 1993 United Feature Syndicate, Inc.
AND HERE THEY ARE

HEY, GARFIELD, I HAVE A JOKE FOR YOU
HA! HA! HA! HA!
DON'T YOU THINK I SHOULD TELL THE JOKE BEFORE YOU LAUGH?
LET'S NOT RUIN THE MOMENT, JON
© 1993 United Feature Syndicate, Inc.
JIM DAVIS 10-12

SAD...
I DON'T HAVE ANYTHING BETTER TO DO THAN THIS
I THINK I WAS JUST INSULTED
© 1993 United Feature Syndicate, Inc.
JIM DAVIS 8-3

IF JON'S PERSONALITY WAS ANY LESS COLORFUL, HE'D BE INVISIBLE
RIGHT, JON?
© 1993 United Feature Syndicate, Inc.
JIM DAVIS 8-7

YOU'RE DISGUSTING, GARFIELD. YOU CLAW THE FURNITURE, EAT ALL THE FOOD, CHASE THE DOG, SHED EVERYWHERE...
AND YOU'RE SELFISH. WHAT DO YOU HAVE TO SAY TO THAT?
I SAVED YOU A BITE OF FERN
© 1993 United Feature Syndicate, Inc.
JIM DAVIS 8-14

HI, ODIE
IF THAT DOG'S BRAIN WERE A CAR, IT WOULD BE JAMMED IN NEUTRAL
JIM DAVIS 12-3
© 1983 United Feature Syndicate, Inc.

WHAT A STRANGE DAY
I DON'T UNDERSTAND IT, GARFIELD
PEOPLE LAUGHED AT MY TIE ALL DAY
ARE YOU SURE IT WASN'T YOUR BUNNY SLIPPERS?
JIM DAVIS 7-10
© 1993 United Feature Syndicate, Inc.

I WANT YOU TO "GET" THAT MOUSE, GARFIELD
I THINK YOU KNOW WHAT I MEAN
YES, I DO
© 1992 United Feature Syndicate, Inc.
HEY, MOUSE! YOUR MOTHER DRESSES YOU FUNNY!
JIM DAVIS 2-18

THIS, STUDENTS, IS THE DOMESTICATED HOUSE CAT.
Z
© 1992 United Feature Syndicate, Inc.
DESCENDANT OF THE MIGHTY LION...
Z
NOW DEGENERATED INTO THIS
SAD
I HAVE A SUDDEN URGE TO WAKE UP AND KILL SOMETHING
JIM DAVIS 2-17

IT SAYS HERE, "PEOPLE WITH PETS LIVE LONGER"
© 1992 United Feature Syndicate, Inc.
MAYBE IT JUST SEEMS LONGER
JIM DAVIS 2-13

HMMPH, ANOTHER MOVIE ABOUT THE HEROIC FEATS OF A KIND-HEARTED, LOVABLE DOG
JIM DAVIS 2-7
WHY IS IT YOU NEVER SEE ANYTHING LIKE THAT ABOUT KIND-HEARTED, LOVABLE CATS?
© 1992 United Feature Syndicate, Inc.
MOVE OR DIE, BEAN BRAIN

BELIEVE IT OR NOT, GARFIELD. THE WORLD DOES **NOT** REVOLVE AROUND YOU!
JIM DAVIS 3-23
© 1992 United Feature Syndicate, Inc.
ALTHOUGH YOU ARE BIG ENOUGH FOR IT TO!
ONE SHOT AT A TIME, PLEASE

WHAT'S GOOD TODAY, IRMA?
JIM DAVIS 3-18
Menu
IRMA
© 1992 United Feature Syndicate, Inc.
WHAT'S EDIBLE TODAY, IRMA?
TRY THE MEAT LOAF

HAVING A DOG CAN PROVIDE A SENSE OF SECURITY
JIM DAVIS 5·27
I SLEEP BETTER AT NIGHT HAVING ODIE AROUND
© 1992 United Feature Syndicate, Inc
YEAH. HE BORES ME TOO

YOU KNOW WHAT'S DISGUSTING?
WHAT?
JIM DAVIS 5·12
© 1992 United Feature Syndicate, Inc.
THINGS COVERED WITH CAT HAIR!
HOW TRUE
HEY, WAIT A MINUTE!

HOW'D YOU LIKE TO BE A BEAR, GARFIELD? EVERY WINTER YOU COULD SLEEP FOUR MONTHS STRAIGHT
DON'T BE RIDICULOUS
JIM DAVIS 6·12
Z
YEAH, THAT WOULD BE CUTTING BACK WOULDN'T IT?!

MOM MADE YOU A TIE FOR YOUR BIRTHDAY, GARFIELD
A TIE?!
OH WELL, I GUESS IT'S THE THOUGHT THAT COUNTS
AND THESE CUFF LINKS
I MUST REMEMBER TO SEND HER A THANK-YOU BOMB
JIM DAVIS 6·16

JIM DAVIS
7-7
THERE YOU HAVE IT...
ODIE'S SO STUPID, HE DOESN'T EVEN UNDERSTAND THE LAW OF GRAVITY

HELLO THERE, MR. LAZY
STICKS AND STONES MAY BREAK MY BONES, BUT WORDS WILL NEVER HURT ME
HOG DANDRUFF!
MY LAWYERS, HOWEVER, FEEL OTHERWISE
JIM DAVIS 6-9

HOW DO YOU LIKE THIS SUIT, GARFIELD?
JIM DAVIS 7-10
© 1992 United Feature Syndicate, Inc.

I REMEMBER THE DAY I PICKED YOU OUT, GARFIELD
JIM DAVIS 7-9
© 1992 United Feature Syndicate, Inc.
IT WAS A TOUGH DECISION
REALLY?
IT WAS BETWEEN YOU OR THE IGUANA
I COULD HAVE LIVED THE REST OF MY LIFE WITHOUT KNOWING THAT, JON

IT SAYS IN THIS CAT BOOK THAT CATS ARE SLEEK, SVELTE ANIMALS
© 1992 United Feature Syndicate, Inc
WHAT HAPPENED TO YOU?
I CAN'T READ! OKAY?!
JIM DAVIS 7-3

DID YOU KNOW CATS CAN TALK? WE JUST DON'T CHOOSE TO
© 1992 United Feature Syndicate, Inc
GARFIELD, I'M HOME!
WHO CARES?!
IF WE DID, **NOBODY** WOULD LIKE US
JIM DAVIS 7-2

I'M SO DULL, I'M ALMOST INVISIBLE
© 1992 United Feature Syndicate, Inc.
WHO SAID THAT?
JIM DAVIS 8-22

LADIES AND GENTLEMEN... MR. EXCITEMENT!
JIM DAVIS 8-17
© 1992 United Feature Syndicate, Inc.
I RECKON IT MIGHT RAIN... UNLESS THE SUN COMES OUT, OF COURSE
GO BACK TO YOUR HOMES! MR. EXCITEMENT HAS SPOKEN!

PEOPLE WHO HAVE SIMPLE PLEASURES SHOULD BE ADMIRED
FUZZY BUNNY SLIPPERS!... CUTE BUNNY SLIPPERS!... COMFY BUNNY SLIPPERS!
...AND THEN EXECUTED
JIM DAVIS 8-10
© 1992 United Feature Syndicate, Inc

HERE COMES ODIE. HIS BARK IS WORSE THAN HIS BITE
BARK! BARK!
BARK!
AND HIS BREATH IS WORSE THAN HIS BARK
JIM DAVIS 7-27
© 1983 United Feature Syndicate, Inc.

YAAAAAHHH!!!
JIM DAVIS 10-5
WHAT A HORRIBLE NIGHTMARE! I DREAMED I LIVED WITH A HUMAN WHO...
YAAAAAAHHHH!!!

THIS IS HAROLD MELSNICK
JIM DAVIS 9-2
HE USED TO CALL ME A LOSER!
THIS IS ME AT THE PROM
LOVELY DRESS YOUR MOTHER IS WEARING

SNEAK
SNEAK
SNEAK
JIM DAVIS 10-27
© 1992 United Feature Syndicate, Inc.
TAP
TAP
SNICKER
SNICKER
YEEEEK!!

ON THIS BEACH YOU HAVE SURF NUTS, BEACH BUMS...
I TOUCHED SEAWEED!!
© 1992 United Feature Syndicate, Inc.
JIM DAVIS 11-25
AND SAND DWEEBS

YOU ARE LAZY, GARFIELD, AND YOU CAN'T DENY IT!
I CAN SO DENY IT!
I JUST DON'T FEEL LIKE IT, THAT'S ALL
JIM DAVIS 12-11

WHEN GARFIELD IS AWAKE, HE'S A FAT DISGUSTING PIG
BUT WHEN HE'S ASLEEP, HE LOOKS JUST LIKE AN ANGEL
Z
A FAT, DISGUSTING ANGEL
JIM DAVIS 12-4

YOU SHOW ME YOUR UGLY MASK, AND I'LL SHOW YOU MINE
JIM DAVIS 10-31

YOU'RE A WORTHLESS LUMP OF BLUBBER, GARFIELD
THAT WASN'T VERY NICE
LUMPS OF BLUBBER HAVE FEELINGS TOO
JIM DAVIS 3-9

BOO!
WELL, YOU'VE BEEN A LOVELY AUDIENCE
BOO!
I'D LIKE TO GIVE YOU ALL A BIG HUG AND A KISS
© 1993 United Feature Syndicate, Inc.
JIM DAVIS 4-24
BOO!
HOW ABOUT A GOOD SLAP AND A LIVE BADGER UP THE NOSE?

WHAT DO YOU GET IF YOU REMOVE HALF A CAT'S BRAIN?
YOU GET A SMART DOG!
JIM DAVIS
4-23
© 1993 United Feature Syndicate, Inc.
THANK YOU! PLEASE HOLD YOUR ADULATION TILL THE END OF THE PERFORMANCE!

HUMANS HAVE MUCH LARGER BRAINS THAN CATS DO
YOU SURE DO...
© 1993 United Feature Syndicate, Inc.
NOW, HOW DOES THIS DOOR WORK?
LARGE AND UNWIELDY
JIM DAVIS 5-18

CHEER UP, GARFIELD. FIFTEEN'S NOT SO OLD...
© 1993 United Feature Syndicate, Inc.
FOR AN OAK TREE!
PAT PAT PAT
JIM DAVIS 6-17

JIM DAVIS 12-19
CHRISTMAS IS A TIME OF TRADITIONS
SOME OLD, SOME NEW, SOME UNIVERSAL...
AND SOME FROM THE LUNATIC FRINGE
C'MON, GARFIELD! PUT YOURS ON!

MEOW?
PARDON?
MEOW MEOW
OKAY, I'LL BITE
MEOW
I'VE COMMUNICATED WITH A LOWER LIFE-FORM!
I'VE BEEN DOING THAT FOR YEARS
JIM DAVIS 5-3

HI, I'M NERMAL. I'M CUTE, AND YOU'RE NOT
I'M YOUNG, AND YOU'RE NOT
© 1993 United Feature Syndicate, Inc.
I'M FEELING FINE, AND YOU'RE NOT
JIM DAVIS 6-15

ODIE, YOU'RE MUCH SMARTER THAN YOU LOOK!
JIM DAVIS 6-9
© 1993 United Feature Syndicate, Inc.
THOUGH HE'S STILL DUMB ENOUGH TO THINK THAT'S A COMPLIMENT

FILLING IN FOR ODIE TODAY WILL BE THIS PIECE OF CARDBOARD!
OH, HI, ODIE
PSSST, TRY TO LOOK DUMBER
JIM DAVIS 6-8
© 1993 United Feature Syndicate, Inc.

THERE'S ODIE'S TONGUE
JIM DAVIS 6-7
THIS PROBABLY MEANS HE'S IN THE BUILDING SOMEWHERE
© 1993 United Feature Syndicate, Inc.

HEY, GARFIELD, YOU'RE GOING TO BE FIFTEEN?! ZOWIE! FIFTEEN!
I DIDN'T KNOW ANYTHING WAS THAT OLD!
© 1993 United Feature Syndicate, Inc.
JIM DAVIS 6-16
DON'T PUSH IT, KID
I MEAN, I THOUGHT DIRT WAS ELEVEN, MAYBE TWELVE YEARS OLD!

MY LEGS!
I CAN'T FEEL MY LEGS!!
© 1991 United Feature Syndicate, Inc.
MEDIC!!!
VERY FUNNY, JON
1-2-92
JIM DAVIS

YOU KNOW, GARFIELD, THE BRAIN IS A MUSCLE
GIVE ME A BREAK
KNOW HOW I KEEP MY MIND SHARP?
A WOOD RASP?
CONNECT THE DOTS!
YOU'RE A REAL INTELLECTUAL
© 1991 United Feature Syndicate, Inc.
JIM DAVIS 12-4

SOMETIMES I FEEL LIKE A LAUGHINGSTOCK, GARFIELD
LOOK! THERE HE IS!
HAW! HAW! HAW!
I'LL BE IN MY ROOM
BIG CROWD TODAY
© 1991 United Feature Syndicate, Inc.
JIM DAVIS 12-5

NOTICE ANYTHING NEW, GARFIELD?
GIVE ME A HINT
DON'T YOU THINK THIS PIPE MAKES ME LOOK MORE SOPHISTICATED?
SADLY ENOUGH, I HAVE TO AGREE
© 1991 United Feature Syndicate, Inc.
JIM DAVIS 12-6

I CALLED TO THANK YOU FOR THE CHRISTMAS GIFT, MOM
YOU REALLY OUTDID YOURSELF THIS TIME
I DIDN'T KNOW YOU COULD CROCHET A SUIT
SOMEONE SHOULD STOP HER
© 1991 United Feature Syndicate, Inc
JIM DAVIS 12-27

LET'S FACE IT...
AS WE AGE, OUR BODIES CHANGE
MY EYEBALLS ARE GROWING HAIR!
OR, IN SOME CASES, MUTATE
© 1991 United Feature Syndicate, Inc.
JIM DAVIS 10-5

WELCOME TO "LYING AROUND WITH GARFIELD"
TODAY'S TOPIC, THE JOY OF CEILING WATCHING
YOU ARE WORTHLESS
NOW LET'S STARE AT A LIGHT FIXTURE
© 1991 United Feature Syndicate, Inc
JIM DAVIS 11-28

THEY SAY ONE'S DINNERWARE SHOULD REFLECT ONE'S PERSONALITY
© 1991 United Feature Syndicate, Inc.
FOR ME, FINE CHINA
FOR YOU, A HOG TROUGH
EVER BEEN BIT BY A PIG?
JIM DAVIS 9-19

GARFIELD, HOW DO YOU EXPLAIN THIS?
© 1991 United Feature Syndicate, Inc
WHEN I WAS YOUNG I SWALLOWED A BASKETBALL
YOU'RE A PIG!
IT'S BEEN DIGESTING FOR YEARS
JIM DAVIS 8-8

© 1991 United Feature Syndicate, Inc
YOU'RE ONE OF A KIND, GARFIELD
JIM DAVIS 8-16
WHY, THANK YOU
AT LEAST THAT'S WHAT THE ENTIRE HUMAN RACE IS HOPING
I HATE YOU

ODIE IS A MIXED BREED
© 1991 United Feature Syndicate, Inc.
HIS MOTHER WAS A BEAGLE
AND HIS FATHER WAS A BRICK
JIM DAVIS 7-31

HEY, GARFIELD. HOW'S THE WEATHER DOWN THERE?
HA!HA! HA!HA!
DRAFTY
© 1991 United Feature Syndicate, Inc
JIM DAVIS 4-6

HEY, ARBUCKLE, YOUR CAT'S IN THE TREE...
© 1991 United Feature Syndicate, Inc.
AND YOU'D BETTER PICK HIM. HE LOOKS A LITTLE TOO RIPE!
HAW! HAW! HAW! HAW!
STEP UNDER ME AND SAY THAT, FELLA!
JIM DAVIS 5-16

WAH-HA! HA! HA!
BOY, HAIRCUTS ARE DECEIVING
© 1991 United Feature Syndicate, Inc.
JIM DAVIS 4-2

TOUCH MY FOOD AND DIE!!
OH, COME ON, JON. YOU'RE NOT THAT BAD OF A COOK
© 1991 United Feature Syndicate, Inc.
JIM DAVIS 3-28

I SUPPOSE YOU CAN FIX BETTER PANCAKES!
© 1991 United Feature Syndicate, Inc
JIM DAVIS 2-8

ETHEL, LOOK AT THAT!
© 1991 United Feature Syndicate, Inc.
WOW!
THAT'S GOTTA BE THE FATTEST ORANGE I EVER SAW!
JIM DAVIS 5-15

YES, NERMAL, LIFE IS A COMPLICATED THING. YOU GET OUT OF IT WHAT YOU PUT INTO IT
5-10
© 1989 United Feature Syndicate, Inc.
THAT WAS PRETTY INTELLECTUAL. ANY QUESTIONS?
IS IT HARD TO TALK WITH SIX CHINS?
I HATE YOU
JIM DAVIS

HERE I STAND ON TOP OF THE WORLD. MASTER OF ALL I SEE
JIM DAVIS
© 1989 United Feature Syndicate, Inc.
NONE DARE CHALLENGE ME, UNLESS OF COURSE THEY BE FOOLS, OR...
5-9

GIDDYAP, YOU FLEA-BITTEN PLUG!
5-11
TO THE CORRAL, YOU WORTHLESS PIECE OF HORSEFLESH!
JIM DAVIS
© 1989 United Feature Syndicate, Inc.
STUPID PET DOOR

ODIE LEFT HIS BRAIN TO SCIENCE
5-26
© 1989 United Feature Syndicate, Inc.
AND THEY MADE AN EARLY WITHDRAWAL
JIM DAVIS

WHEW
© 1989 United Feature Syndicate, Inc.
BANZAI!
YAAAH!
JIM DAVIS
6-6

THIS DAY IS THE DULLEST...
© 1989 United Feature Syndicate, Inc.
THINGS CAN'T GET MORE BORING THAN THIS...
ANY MORE STAMPS AROUND HERE?
BINGO
JIM DAVIS
9-13

WORRIED ABOUT WRINKLES, GARFIELD?
JIM DAVIS
JUST REMEMBER, WRINKLES ONLY EXIST TO SHOW WHERE THE SMILES HAVE BEEN
© 1989 United Feature Syndicate, Inc.
YOUR LIFE MUST BE A LAUGH RIOT
OH, SHUT UP
7-28

LIKE MY TIE, GARFIELD?
WELL, I...
JIM DAVIS 8-11
© 1989 United Feature Syndicate, Inc.
YOU IN THE HOUSE... YOU ARE SURROUNDED!
OH NO! IT'S THE GEEK POLICE!
THROW OUT THE TIE!

I CAN'T BELIEVE IT. TWO WEEKS COOPED UP WITH JON AND ODIE IN THE MIDDLE OF NOWHERE
8-28
IF I DON'T GET TO VISIT WITH SOME REAL HUMANITY SOON, I'M GOING TO GO STARKERS!
© 1989 United Feature Syndicate, Inc.
SO... ROCK, READ ANY GOOD BOOKS LATELY?
JIM DAVIS

WELL, IF IT ISN'T NERMAL, THE WORLD'S CUTEST KITTEN
IN PERSON
TELL ME... HOW IS IT YOU'VE UH, YOU'VE...
I'VE STAYED THE SAME WHILE YOU'VE WITHERED LIKE A TWO-YEAR-OLD CANTALOUPE?
© 1989 United Feature Syndicate, Inc.
ARRRGH
IF YOU NAIL'EM HARD, THERE'S PLENTY OF TIME FOR A GETAWAY
JIM DAVIS
7-25

I FEEL DOWN TODAY, GARFIELD
OH, 'DEM BLUES. DEY DONE GOT ME DOWN. OH, YEAH
SOMETIMES I JUST GOTTA LET IT OUT
I WAS HOPING WE'D HAVE TO OPERATE
3-6
© 1989 United Feature Syndicate, Inc.
JIM DAVIS

HEY! I WAS GOING TO SIT THERE, GARFIELD
GET LOST
HEY!
GET LOST
© 1989 United Feature Syndicate, Inc.
JIM DAVIS
4-17

IT'S BEEN OVER A WEEK AND ODIE STILL HASN'T OPENED HIS CHRISTMAS PRESENT
OH WELL, HE'LL FIGURE IT OUT ONE OF THESE DAYS
© 1990 United Feature Syndicate, Inc
I THINK YOU OVERESTIMATE HIM
JIM DAVIS 1-3-91

JON'S SENDING AWAY FOR A BOOK
IT'S CALLED "HELP FOR THE INCOMPETENT"
© 1990 United Feature Syndicate, Inc
I THINK THESE STAMPS ARE DEFECTIVE
JUST IN TIME
JIM DAVIS 12-5

DOC BOY! HOW ARE YOU?
DON'T CALL ME DOC BOY!
OH, SORRY. HMMM WHAT ELSE DID I USED TO CALL YOU?...
© 1989 United Feature Syndicate, Inc.
OH, YEAH! IGUANA GUMS! HOW ARE YOU?
CALL ME DOC BOY
JIM DAVIS 7-11

HI THERE, I'M JON ARBUCKLE. THIS IS MY FIRST NIGHT IN POTTERY CLASS. WHAT ARE YOU MAKING?
A MAN!
IT DOESN'T LOOK MUCH LIKE A MAN
© 1990 United Feature Syndicate, Inc.
WELL, WHATEVER IT IS, IT'S A DARN SIGHT BETTER THAN MY FOURTH HUSBAND WALDO!
POOR WALDO
JIM DAVIS 11-22

SEEING A MAGNIFICENT UNIVERSE SUCH AS THIS MAKES ME FEEL LIKE AN INSIGNIFICANT, SPECK
JIM DAVIS 10-20
HOW ABOUT YOU, GARFIELD?
YOU'RE RIGHT
© 1989 United Feature Syndicate, Inc.
I THINK YOU'RE AN INSIGNIFICANT SPECK TOO

SOME TASTELESS PEOPLE WEAR CLIP-ON TIES
10-4
JIM DAVIS
© 1989 United Feature Syndicate, Inc.
JON WEARS CLIP-ON **SUITS**

YOU'RE WORTHLESS, GARFIELD
NOTHING WILL EVER BECOME OF YOU LYING THERE LIKE THAT
HEY! HEY! MICHELANGELO PAINTED THE SISTINE CHAPEL LIKE THIS, FELLA!
© 1990 United Feature Syndicate, Inc.
JIM DAVIS 8-13

YOU'RE FAT
JIM DAVIS
10-6
YOUR FINGER IS FAT TOO
© 1990 United Feature Syndicate, Inc.
EVEN YOUR WHISKER IS FAT
GIMME A BREAK

© 1990 United Feature Syndicate, Inc.
I AM PERSONALLY LOOKING FORWARD TO COLDER WEATHER
JIM DAVIS
6-20

ARR! ARR! ARR!
NO SWEAT
© 1990 United Feature Syndicate, Inc.
DOGS ARE TOO STUPID TO CLIMB TREES
JIM DAVIS 9-26
CHOP CHOP CHOP CHOP

YOU KNOW, WE'RE BOTH GETTING PRETTY PORKY LATELY, GARFIELD
OINK OINK
JIM DAVIS 6-9
GARFIELD
© 1990 United Feature Syndicate, Inc.
I THINK WE SHOULD DIET TOGETHER
DIET TOGETHER BY YOURSELF
GARFIELD
AFTER ALL, "MISERY LOVES COMPANY"
IS YOUR FAMILY COMING FOR A VISIT?
GARFIELD

GUESS WHAT, GARFIELD?
© 1990 United Feature Syndicate, Inc.
YOUR LIFE IS HOPELESSLY POINTLESS?
I THINK MY BUNNY SLIPPERS ARE IN LOVE!
I STAND CORRECTED
JIM DAVIS 7-27

JIM DAVIS 9-2
© 1994 PAWS, INC/Distributed by Universal Press Syndicate
AREN'T YOU GOING TO TRY TO GET ME?
I'M CUTTING DOWN ON THE FAT IN MY DIET
YOU **ARE** VICIOUS

GARFIELD, YOU EAT ENOUGH TO FEED THREE CATS
GARFIELD
JIM DAVIS
© 1990 United Feature Syndicate, Inc.
I KNOW, JON, AND I'M SO ASHAMED
GARFIELD
NOW BE A GOOD BOY AND FETCH DESSERT
I'M GLAD WE HAD THIS TALK
3-23

© 1990 United Feature Syndicate, Inc.
WAS THAT AN ECLIPSE?
JIM DAVIS 7-4
OH, IT WAS JUST GARFIELD WALKING PAST THE WINDOW
SHADDUP

DO YOU REALIZE I'M YOUR BEST FRIEND, GARFIELD?
© 1990 United Feature Syndicate, Inc.
OH, NO!
WHAT HAPPENED TO THE PIZZA DELIVERY BOY?!
JIM DAVIS 3-20

GARFIELD, HAVE YOU SEEN MY STRIPED TIE? I CAN'T FIND IT ANYWHERE!
OH WELL, I GUESS I'LL JUST HAVE TO WEAR MY POLKA DOT TIE INSTEAD
© 1989 United Feature Syndicate, Inc.
JIM DAVIS 12-7
♪
NOW HE'S A DIP COMING **AND** GOING

JIM DAVIS 8-28
© 1990 United Feature Syndicate, Inc.
CHECKING FOR A PULSE
I HATE THAT

WHAT KIND OF DOG IS THAT, JON?
WELL, DAD... HE'S, UH...
I HAVE A HUNCH
WHAT'S THAT?
WORTHLESS
© 1990 United Feature Syndicate, Inc.
7-18
JIM DAVIS

I HAVE A JOB FOR YOU, GARFIELD
YOU ARE NOW MY PAPERWEIGHT
WHEN'S COFFEE BREAK?
© 1990 United Feature Syndicate, Inc.
JIM DAVIS 8-30

LOOK, GARFIELD. I'VE HAD MY PORTRAIT DONE!
JON
JIM DAVIS 4-2
© 1990 United Feature Syndicate, Inc.
I'LL GET THE DARTS

THERE'S SOMETHING SPECIAL ABOUT GETTING MAIL, GARFIELD
JIM DAVIS 5-9
© 1990 United Feature Syndicate, Inc.
IT'S NICE TO KNOW SOMEONE'S THINKING OF YOU
DEAR DEADBEAT, SEND A PAYMENT OR I'LL REPOSSESS YOUR TEETH
FROM YOUR BROTHER! HOW SWEET!

HACK! COUGH! THE WEIGHT'S TOO MUCH! I'M A GONER!
LEAN OVER. I WANT TO SEE YOUR FACE BEFORE I GO...
© 1994 PAWS, INC./Distributed by Universal Press Syndicate
OR IS THAT YOUR FACE?...
THIS IS CALLED JUSTIFIABLE HOMICIDE
JIM DAVIS 8-20

YOU KNOW, THERE'S "FAT"...
AND THEN THERE'S "FAT- FAT"
SO WHAT AM I?
© 1994 PAWS, INC./Distributed by Universal Press Syndicate
"FAT-FAT-FAT-FAT-FAT-FAT-FAT-FAT-FAT-FAT-FAT-FAT-FAT-FAT-FAT-FAT-FAT-FAT-FAT-FAT-FAT-FAT-FAT-FAT-FAT-FAT-FAT-FAT-FAT-FAT-FAT-"
JIM DAVIS 8-16